Be Patien

MANNERS ALWAYS MATTER

Illustrated by Lance Raichert
Written by Jason Blundy

Copyright © 2005 Publications International, Ltd. All rights reserved.
This publication may not be reproduced in whole or in part by
any means whatsoever without written permission from
Louis Weber, C.E.O., Publications International, Ltd.
7373 North Cicero Avenue, Lincolnwood, Illinois 60712
Ground Floor, 59 Gloucester Place, London W1U 8JJ
www.pilbooks.com
Permission is never granted for commercial purposes.
Manufactured in China.
ISBN 1-4127-3005-8

On a beautiful summer morning Puppy set out on his tricycle to meet his friends at the park.

Puppy had been riding his tricycle for a while, but he still found it a little hard to get around.

He was determined, though, and looked forward to riding through the park with his friends.

When he got to the park he was amazed to see his friends riding bicycles.

"What's going on?" asked Puppy.

"We got new bikes," said Hippo, "so we can zoom around faster than ever!"

"That's nice," said Puppy, "but I don't think I'll be able to keep up with you guys."

Sadly, Puppy headed home with his tricycle.

On the way home, Puppy stopped by the bicycle shop and stared at all of the nice, new bikes in the store.

"I'll never be able to ride one of those," thought Puppy. "I have a hard enough time with my tricycle. It's not fair. I just want to be able to ride around with my friends."

Puppy pouted as he pedaled away from the bike shop.

At home, Puppy was sitting out on the curb when his friends strolled up with a bicycle that had a huge bow on it.

"Look, Puppy!" yelled Kitty excitedly. "We were so sad that you couldn't play with us today, we decided to pool our money together and get you a bicycle. Now we can all ride our bicycles together!"

They hurried back to the park and put training wheels on Puppy's bike to make learning easier for him. He tried to keep up, but Puppy struggled to get the hang of it.

"Isn't this fun?" squealed Piggy with delight.

"This is impossible!" cried Puppy. "I'll never be able to ride as well as you guys."

Hippo rode by and saw Puppy all by himself.

"What's the matter?" Hippo asked.

"This is just too hard," said Puppy. "I'll never be able to ride like you."

Hippo tried to cheer up his little friend.

"Don't be silly," he said. "Be patient and you'll learn in no time at all. Here. Why don't you let me help you?"

Puppy practiced and practiced. After a while they took off his training wheels.

Puppy struggled, but finally, after a push start by Hippo, Puppy felt like he had it. He looked back and saw that he had already zoomed away from his friends. They were cheering in the distance.

"I knew you could do it," yelled Hippo. "You just had to be patient."

Be Patient

Sometimes we have a hard time learning, but it's important to be patient. Puppy could have given up, but he didn't. He learned to be patient and before long he was able to ride as well as his friends.